Bonawe Furnace

Geoffrey P Stell
and
Geoffrey D Hay

HISTORIC SCOTLAND

ISBN 1 900168 03 0

Bunaw · F · JJ53

Aerial view of the ironworks from south looking towards Lorn quay on Loch Etive. (See also page 18.)

'The longest-lived blast-furnace in the Scottish Highlands'

The extensive and well-preserved remains of Bonawe Iron Furnace constitute one of the most notable monuments of the iron industry in Britain. The ironworks was established here in 1752-3 and formed an offshoot of a parent company based in the Furness district of Lancashire (now in Cumbria). Bonawe was the penultimate, probably the largest, and certainly the longest-lived of the charcoal blast-furnaces in the Scottish Highlands, and production continued here, albeit intermittently in the later phases, until 1876.

This area contained abundant and relatively cheap sources of woodland suitable for the manufacture of good quality charcoal, the principal fuel employed in the iron smelting process before the more widespread use of coke from the second half of the eighteenth century onwards. This site was particularly well placed for the water-borne transport of materials on Loch Etive, and could rely on the water of the River Awe to provide the necessary motive-power to drive the blast-furnace. During this phase of the industry it was cheaper to move the iron ore to the source of the charcoal. The ore was thus mainly imported from Furness and Central Scotland, and, in the absence of a forge, the principal finished products were cast-iron 'pigs' exported back to England.

The ironworks formed a self-contained and isolated industrial community complete with workers' housing, school and church (see illustration on page 18). While local people were employed, especially in the manufacture of charcoal, the workforce included a substantial proportion of English immigrants, although, in the opinion of one contemporary, 'Englishmen do not thrive here'. The buildings themselves also betray the origins of the company and its early craftsmen in the manner in which some of them have been constructed.

The first part of this guide describes the processes of iron smelting and charcoal manufacture, which are essential for a full understanding of the monument, and then sets the history of Bonawe against the general background of the iron industry in Britain.

The second part is a descriptive tour (pages 19-27) commencing at the storage sheds and dealing in turn with the principal surviving industrial buildings. There is a brief supplementary description of the associated domestic and other structures which formed part of the original complex but which lie outside the area in the care of the State. Visitors to the site are asked to respect the private ownership and occupation of these adjacent lands and buildings.

Bunaw · F · 1753

An early water-powered blast-furnace; detail from 'Meuse landscape with mine and blast-furnaces' by Lucas van Valkenborch, 1580.

'It gives employment to near 600 hands'

IRON SMELTING

Iron smelting is an ancient process that dates from the second millennium B.C. Its general purpose is to convert raw iron ore (mainly iron oxide) to a workable and usable metallic iron by a process of reduction. The ore is heated and combined with carbon in order to release the oxygen that is present.

Bloomeries

The earliest smelting operations evidently involved heating a mass of ore for a few hours in a charcoal fire. It formed a spongy red hot mass of iron known as a 'bloom' which was then repeatedly hammered and reheated to remove the slag and other impurities. These small-scale bloomeries, as they are commonly known, now generally survive as mounds of slag comprising cinders and charcoal; they may have operated with a forced or induced draught, perhaps with some form of hand-operated bellows, and they may have had some provision for tapping the slag.

Charcoal blast-furnaces

In western Europe in the later Middle Ages it was discovered almost by accident that the blast from a sizeable furnace with mechanically-operated bellows raised the temperature sufficiently high (that is, over 1200°C) to produce an alloy of iron and carbon which could be run off from the base of the furnace in liquid form. It was tapped from the furnace hearth into an elongated furrow prepared in a bed of sand. This principal mould was termed the 'sow', and, continuing this porcine metaphor (that is, a sow and its litter), the lesser branches which ran from it at intervals were appropriately known as 'pigs', hence pig iron. These rough bars of hard and brittle cast iron might then be sent to foundries and forges to be further

Tapping the furnace and casting 'pigs' (from Diderot's Encyclopédie, 1763).

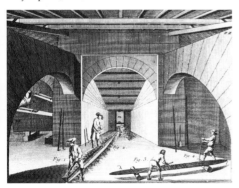

Tapping the furnace and founding cast-iron articles (from Diderot's Encyclopédie, 1763).

refined into malleable or wrought iron. The furnace could be combined with a foundry, and some objects could be cast directly from the furnace, the molten metal being carefully ladled by hand.

In principle, these charcoal blast-furnaces continued to operate on simple long-established lines, although on a larger and more commercial scale. The furnace-shaft or chimney was fed from above with measured proportions of charcoal, iron ore and a flux, and the chimney was flared in such a manner as to ensure that the contents, or charge, were slowly but continuously descending. The flux—limestone by the time Bonawe was operating—helped remove non-metallic impurities. The complex chemical reactions were maintained by an upward blast of air supplied by a pair of water-powered bellows blowing alternately, and subsequently in some cases by steam-operated cylinders. The aim was to allow the dense molten iron to trickle down through the charge to the hearth where it would settle, with the slag floating on top of it, prior to being drawn off. The contributor to Diderot's *Encyclopédie* of 1763 picturesquely likens the furnace to 'a stomach which demands feeding steadily, regularly and endlessly. It is subject to changes in behaviour through lack of nourishment, to indigestion and embarrassing eruptions through too rich or voluminous a diet, and in such cases prompt remedies are to be applied'. The various parts of the furnace's anatomy and digestive system are given technical terms which are further explained in the detailed description of the Bonawe Furnace.

Charging the blast-furnace (from Diderot's Encyclopédie, *1763).*

CHARCOAL

Charcoal supply

During the charcoal phase of the iron industry it was the presence of trees, rather than of iron ore, that determined the siting of blast-furnaces, for it proved cheaper to move ore over long distances than charcoal. Charcoal is a friable commodity, fairly easily crushed or shaken to powder, and some wastage was probably allowed for when it was being transported and stored. Thus, for example, a proposal to export Galloway charcoal by sea to Furness in the late eighteenth century freely acknowledged that about one quarter of the intended cargo would not be usable on arrival. The wastage rate resulting from contemporary land transport would be even higher. One of the main aims of the ironmasters, therefore, was to minimise these difficulties, and within the neighbourhood of the ironworks there was every reason for them to utilise local woodland resources efficiently by an intensive process of rotational coppicing. Long-term contracts for local wood rights were thus an essential prelude to any proposed ironwork operation, and, as needs arose, these resources could be supplemented by short-term contracts further afield, preferably within easy reach of waterborne means of transport. Coppice oak evidently made the best coalwood, and the contracts usually conveyed rights over the bark, which could be stored and used or exported for tanning purposes.

The 'coals', as the charcoal was known, were usually supplied in 'dozens', that is, twelve sacks weighing 17 cwt altogether and almost 1·5 cwt each. On the basis of the Bonawe operations, it has been calculated that 1 acre of well-managed coppice could provide 2·34 'dozens' of charcoal, and, making due allowances for wastage, this figure is just about the amount of charcoal required to make 1 ton of pig iron. On a system of optimum coppice rotation (that is, in this part of the world, 20 years) it has thus been estimated that Bonawe Furnace required at least 10,000 acres of deciduous woodlands for sustained operation.

Charcoal manufacture

These figures are partly based on the known fact that deciduous woods yield about one-sixth or thereabouts of their weight in charcoal. In other words, the traditional earth clamp kiln required between 6 and 8 tons of wood to produce 1 ton of lump charcoal. It was thus more

Methods of constructing charcoal kilns (from Diderot's Encyclopédie, *1763).*

Charcoal burning (from Diderot's Encyclopédie, *1763).*

convenient and practicable to carry out the process of manufacture actually in the woodlands, rather than by bringing the wood to the furnace for 'coaling'. The kilns were usually set on a level earthen platform or hearth some 4·5m in diameter. According to more recent practice of these traditional methods elsewhere in Britain, logs varying in length from 500mm to 2m and from 50mm to 200mm in girth are carefully stacked around a central stake, and covered with vegetation and earth. The central stake is removed, leaving a space where the kindled fire is placed and then sealed over. The burning process continues for a period varying between 2–10 days depending on the nature and dryness of the wood, the best results being obtained from wood that has been seasoned to a moisture content of 20 per cent or less.

Charcoal-burning stances or platforms, whose archaeological remains roughly correspond with the dimensions given above, are found in many of the natural woodlands around the western seaboard of Argyll. Their density testifies to the importance of this seasonal industry, and their distribution reflects the remarkably wide area from which Bonawe is known to have drawn its fuel supply.

Constructing a charcoal kiln in the Forest of Dean about 1909-12.

Charcoal burning in the Forest of Dean about 1909-1912.

HISTORY

In Britain commercial production of cast iron in charcoal-fuelled blast-furnaces was actively prosecuted from the late sixteenth century onwards. Furnace operation demanded good supplies of iron ore, wood for the charcoal fuel, and a reliable source of water-power. The English industry was first centred on the Weald but later spread to outlying areas such as the Forest of Dean and Furness where the vital ingredients for iron smelting were also to be found.

The iron industry in the Scottish Highlands

The vast timber resources of the Scottish Highlands provided a cheap and relatively abundant fuel supply that was clearly a major attraction to English and Irish ironmasters in the seventeenth and eighteenth centuries. Iron ores were usually imported from other parts of Scotland and from Furness, but use was also occasionally made of local low-grade bog ore. The first of these commercial enterprises commenced shortly before 1610 when a colony of English workmen under the direction and management of Sir George Hay was 'making iron and casting cannon' among the woods of Letterewe in Gairloch parish, Wester Ross. Iron smelting is also known to have been taking place in Lochaber later in the seventeenth century, but a much more active interest in the area was awakened in the first half of the eighteenth century when no less than four ironworks were established in quick succession between about 1718 and 1728.

Even the earliest of these seventeenth- and eighteenth-century ironworks were probably based on blast-furnace and not bloomery operations. None, however, was particularly long-lived, and, apart from some remains in the Gairloch district and the site at Glen Kinglass, they have left few physical traces. The works at Glen Kinglass, which stood close to the shore of upper Loch Etive, was founded and run by an Irish co-partnership from about 1722 to its closure around 1738. Sir Duncan Campbell of Lochnell was proprietor of the lands of Glen Kinglass, and became more involved in the company's timber enterprises during its short active existence. Undeterred by its failure, and perhaps profiting from his experience, in 1752 he saw fit to enter into agreements with another group of ironmasters, this time from Furness. He granted them a long-term lease of the Glen Kinglass woods and a furnace site at Bonawe, some 9km to the south-west of the original works on Loch Etive.

General view of Glen Kinglass Furnace from west (furnace stack in centre of picture).

Glen Kinglass furnace during excavation, 1979. View from casting-house looking towards the furnace hearth.

Craleckan Furnace, Argyll.

Bonawe Furnace (1753) and the Argyle or Craleckan Furnace (1754) in Mid Argyll represent a mid-eighteenth century phase of iron-working activity and, as matters turned out, they were to be the final, largest and most successful charcoal iron establishments in the Scottish Highlands. Craleckan was founded by the Duddon Furnace Company, a rival concern from Furness, and, like Bonawe, the ironworks continued production into the nineteenth century, until 1813 at least. The supplies of fuel and iron ore were organised on similar lines, but, unlike its counterpart at Bonawe, the Craleckan works eventually came to possess a forge as well as a casting plant.

The signatures of Richard Ford, ironmaster, and other partners in the Newland Company instrumental in establishing Bonawe Furnace in 1753.

History of Bonawe Iron Furnace

The furnace was founded in 1752/3 by Richard Ford and Company, a small partnership, sometimes later known as the Newland Company, which possessed iron mines and charcoal furnaces around Ulverston in Furness. Two agreements for a 110-year lease of wood rights and the site of an ironworks were concluded with Sir Duncan Campbell of Lochnell in September 1752, and the all-important long-term supply of wood was further ensured by a similar contract with the Earl of Breadalbane. The company was to pay £1500 in 10 yearly instalments for the first cutting of the Lochnell woods, and the annual rent for the furnace site was £415, to which was added an entry fine of £243, payable at the end of every 19-year term.

Construction work (and possibly the first iron smelting operations) was undertaken in 1753, the date recorded on the furnace lintels. Richard Ford, the principal figure in the company, died four years later and is commemorated by a mural plaque in Ulverston Parish Church. He was succeeded by his son, William, after whose death in 1769, control of the company's affairs passed to William's sons-in-law, George Knott and Henry Ainslie. George

Knott, who also happened to be son of one of the original associates, died in 1784, and Matthew Harrison of Waterhead, one of the trustees of his will, acquired 'sole management and direction of the concern', eventually buying up the Knott shares in the business. At Matthew Harrison's death in 1824 the Newland firm had become known as Harrison, Ainslie and Company, and by 1828 had obtained control of the entire Furness charcoal iron industry.

The original lease of the company's Scottish wood rights and lands expired in 1863 and a fresh 21-year lease was negotiated with Alexander Kelly of Bonawe. He sub-let the furnace to the ironworks company, but otherwise retained the lands in his possession and undertook to supply the charcoal himself. This second lease failed to run its full term, however, for iron production at Bonawe finally ceased in 1876. By that date Newland and Backbarrow were the only other British charcoal blast-furnaces remaining in operation, and both belonged to the Newland Company.

During its productive life, Bonawe Furnace was administered from Newland through an agent resident at the works. The degree of control that was sometimes necessary to deal with conditions in the distant outpost is shown by the correspondence of George Knott. In March 1781 he wrote to his agent complaining that the furnace quay had acquired notoriety at Oban for being 'the principal smuggling harbour', and he demanded measures to stop the smuggling. 'Put a stop, if possible', he also wrote 'to that confounded drinking in general, and by your shewing the example it may be more easily done, for I believe there is not such another drunken hole in the Kingdom'. The local manager or steward was in charge of a staff which included a wood agent with his small team of assistants and a furnace master with six or seven labourers. In addition to the other agents and craftsmen under his direction, a temporary labour-force of anything up to

11

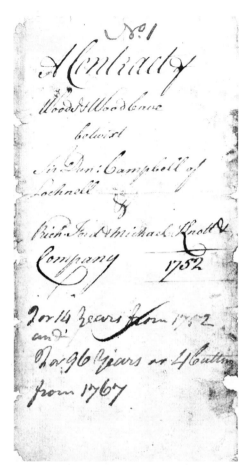

Contract with the Earl of Breadalbane for the delivery of charcoal, 1752.

Contract with Sir Duncan Campbell of Lochnell for the lease of wood rights, 1752.

600 persons might also be employed in the seasonal manufacture and transport of charcoal.

Unfortunately, the extant records of the company's business affairs are incomplete, and relate mainly to the period between 1786 and 1812. Returns show that the furnace was then capable of an annual production of 600–700 tons of pig iron, an average of almost 2 tons per day. The rate had fallen to 400 tons in 1839 and the furnace was out of blast altogether in the years 1859–62, 1864–7 and 1872. Most pigs were shipped to Furness, the Severn estuary and south Wales, and production

was deliberately intended to complement the output from the Furness ironworks. Thus no forge or secondary plant was built but shot was evidently cast when required. In 1781, for instance, 230 tons of ammunition comprising 42,000 '3 to 32 pounder round shot' were supplied by the Newland and Bonawe Furnaces and shipped from Ulverston to the Office of Ordnance at Woolwich.

It has been estimated that pig iron produced at Bonawe cost an average of about £6·50 per ton as compared with £6·75 at Newland. The main saving was in the considerably lower price of charcoal which

Examples of the main products made at Bonawe – a cannon-ball and a length of pig iron marked with the Lorn Company's name.

more than offset the higher transport costs involved in importing the ore and exporting the pigs. The contracts of 1752 permitted a periodic supply of fuel at fixed rates, but the supplementary short-term contracts, which usually covered periods of one or two years, followed the general rise in the price of charcoal. In the later 1780s when detailed records first became available some 80–90 per cent of the fuel came from these more expensive sources, and the charcoal was shipped from woodlands as far away as 64km, as the crow flies, from the furnace. Limestone for use as a flux was quarried locally, probably on the island of Lismore.

A by-product of the charcoal industry was oak bark which was used for tanning. The original contracts included rights over the bark and had provisions for 'making Barkhouses Boats and other accommodation requisite for keeping preserving transporting and manufacturing the said Oak Barks'. In its heyday the company exported barks to tanneries on the Clyde and in north Lancashire. When iron production at Bonawe ceased, some of the furnace buildings themselves were converted for leather tanning but these operations lasted only a short time.

Another subsidiary industry was the spinning of wool into yarn by the workmen's wives. Much of the material was shipped to Furness and thence to Kendal, but in the opinion of George Knott in 1783 'the yarn is a very considerable losing concern. I therefore think that none should be encouraged, or any spinning let out but to such as are real good and necessary families about the works . . . by no means let it be an object as a branch of the business, but as a step necessary to prevent the workmen running into debt'.

The 'real good and necessary families' were housed in the solidly-built dwellings of stone and slate that still form a part of the furnace complex. There were, however, the usual housing problems, and it was reported on one occasion that one of the workmen 'must go into some coal house [that is, a charcoal burner's hut] this winter as his house he now lives in is not fit for a swine on a wet day'. The houses were associated with a system of crofts and allotments in which the workmen were encouraged to apply themselves to the rules and practice of good husbandry. They were also allowed to possess cows and could obtain a lease of grazing rights on the company's land. The overcrowding and misuse of available land was, however, a problem which seriously vexed George Knott. In August 1782 he asserted that 'having such a number of weavers, taylors, etc, and such like useless people is what chiefly crowds the grass with cattle and breeds mischief amongst the useful people', a point which he was obliged to repeat with even more brutal frankness over a year later when he considered 'it most advisable to discharge every useless family and widow'.

The company did, however, exercise some relief for cases of hardship and illness among the 'useful' people. The benevolence also extended to a fairly liberal allowance of whisky or ale. The workmen's families thus became tied to a system of privileges and payments in kind. Together with many other families in the neighbourhood they were dependent on the company's supply of oatmeal which

Main range of workers' housing from the south, about 1965.

Muckairn Churchyard, headstone of Duncan McCalman (d 1959) 'upwards of 39 years iron founder in Lorn Furnace'.

was dispensed at the mealstore (now Shore Cottage). But some of the imported meal was of indifferent quality, judging by a report that 'here are fervent prayers offered up by the poor that Richardson's meal (if no better than formerly) may sink before it arrives at Lorn Quay'.

If local tradition is correct, a similar mood of despair must have run through the furnace community during the French invasion scare of 1797–8. For, having received rumours of the presence of French ships nearby, the company is said to have dumped its stock of cannon balls into the pond in the gardens of Bonawe House lest they fall into enemy hands. In a rather more heroic and proud vein, although betraying a somewhat cavalier disregard for the monuments of antiquity, the workmen

Carron Ironworks, Falkirk, late nineteenth century.

later removed a large prehistoric standing stone from the field behind Airds Bay House and re-erected it about a mile to the east on Cnoc Aingeal, a prominent hillock to the north of Muckairn Parish Church in Tayside village. The inscription on the stone reads: 'To the memory of Lord Nelson this stone was errected [*sic*] by the Lorn Furnace workmen 1805'.

Later developments in the iron industry

Bonawe, although one of the grandest, was also among the very last ironworks in this charcoal-based phase of the industry. The manufacture of coke-smelted iron had been presaged by the successful efforts of Abraham Darby at Coalbrookdale in 1709, and became more widespread in the third quarter of the eighteenth century just as operations were getting under way at Bonawe. The first and greatest Scottish establishment to use coke blast-furnaces with steam-powered blowing engines was the celebrated Ironworks at Carron, near Falkirk, and, because ironstone and coal suitable for conversion to coke often occurred in the same geological measures, the centres of the iron industry thereafter became more closely linked to the coal-fields than to the woodlands. However, coke-smelted pigs still required charcoal for conversion into bar iron until Henry Cort perfected the puddling furnace and rolling process in 1784.

The general drift of the industry towards the coal measures was not quite so pronounced in Scotland until after 1828. In that year James Neilson patented a technique of pre-heating the blast air, and the resultant 'hot blast' permitted fuller use of the low-grade coals and blackband ironstone resources that were more commonly to be found together in Scotland.

Panoramic view from north by G D Hay, 1975. In the words of J M Richards (The Functional Tradition in Early Industrial Buildings, 1958, 21) *'these early industrial buildings . . . were not, for the most part, consciously designed to please. That they are, in fact, pleasing to our eyes is due to the many good qualities they share with other buildings in the functional tradition. . . . They have a clarity of form and a subtle modelling of solids and voids. . . . Then there is their expressive use of materials and their trimness of detail. In fact they display, unobscured by the irrelevances of ornament, the essential attributes of architecture'.*

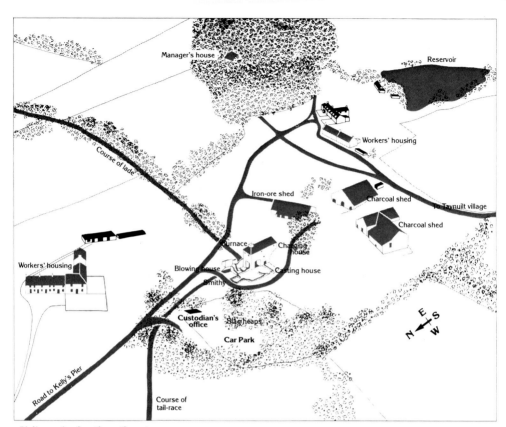

Bird's-eye view from the north-west.

Section showing fall in ground level from (right to left) charcoal shed, ironore shed and furnace.

'Early Industrial Buildings in the Functional Tradition'

T he buildings are here described in the order in which visitors are encouraged to view them. The visitor should note the local topography of the site which slopes, sometimes steeply, from south to north, thus providing the changes in ground level that assisted what was essentially a gravity-feed process and made the best use of available water-power. The principal ingredients—the iron ore, charcoal and limestone—were stored on the higher ground to the south, the storage sheds and the furnace itself being built into the hillside for ease of loading from above at the rear and discharging from the front.

The detailed descriptions that follow are concerned mainly with the purpose and layout of the individual buildings. Much interest and importance also attaches to their structural characteristics and detailing, but, in order to avoid undue repetition, the most conspicuous and idiosyncratic features of building construction have been brought together in a separate section at the end.

Layout of the main buildings.

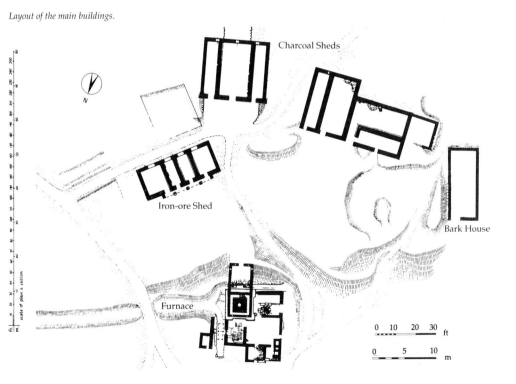

Eastern charcoal shed from north-east.

Charcoal sheds

The charcoal sheds or 'coal houses' are the barn-like structures that stand to the south and south-west of the furnace. In order to achieve the most beneficial results in the working of the furnace the charcoal had to be carefully loaded, stacked and kept in a relatively dry, well-ventilated atmosphere. The buildings are in fact demonstrably large and airy, and ventilation is assisted by the small square apertures in the walls, which may in part also have served as sockets for a system of wooden storage-racks. The surviving sheds together have a total capacity of 2,663 cubic metres, but there would clearly be practical limits to the heights to which the bags of charcoal could be stacked.

Storage of the charcoal was doubtless accorded a high priority in the earliest building-programme but there is no clear evidence for the date and building

sequence of the existing sheds. It is conceivable that the charcoal may initially have been stored in low timber buildings, as was the usual practice in Sweden and found to be the case at Glen Kinglass, and it may have come to be housed in stone-built structures only as the state of business permitted the investment. On the other hand, the western group of sheds bear a distinct likeness to those at Duddon Bridge in Furness, which probably date from the second quarter of the eighteenth century. The eastern shed at Bonawe, despite its central and indeed axial position, is altogether more stylish and technically accomplished in its construction, and may date from a slightly later and more confident phase of building and commercial activity.

As with the other principal buildings, the sheds are built into the hillside for ease of loading from the rear and emptying from

Iron-ore shed from west.

the front. The eastern shed formerly had three pointed-arch unloading doors of slightly differing forms, the most easterly of which was subsequently widened and lintelled. Wooden channel-rails were set into the cobbled floor within, possibly to form a barrel-run. The apex of the south gable-wall is surmounted by a brick stack, probably the remains of a ridge belfry housing the works bell.

The western shed is a composite structure consisting of two two-chambered buildings placed at right angles to each other. The vestiges of a third and smaller unit, possibly another charcoal store, are attached to the west gable-wall. There are also foundations of a large rectangular building of unknown function situated further to the west, while the footings of a small oblong structure lie immediately to the north-east of the entrance to the west shed. One of these at least may have been the 'barkhouse' for the storage of the oak bark required for tanning.

Iron-ore shed

Situated a short distance to the north-east of the eastern charcoal shed and aligned slightly athwart the general slope of the hillside is the long building with a verandah that was used to store the iron ore. Haematite ores that had been shipped from Furness and carboniferous ores from central Scotland were presumably transported up the hill from the jetty in carts and unloaded into the shed through the high-level doors at the rear. The haematite ores generally contained a higher proportion of iron and were reddish in colour, hence the stains on the internal wall-surfaces. When required, the ore was barrowed out of the front doors and across to the furnace.

As originally built the shed comprised three storage bays of unequal size and measured 15·5m by 9m overall. At a later date, when productivity and the market seemingly justified the investment, a fourth and larger bay (now housing the exhibition) was added at the north-east end which extended the overall length of the building to nearly 23m. An open verandah or awning supported on strutted timber posts was also added to provide a sheltered working area at the front. It is likely that the limestone flux was also stored here.

21

General view of furnace from north-west by W Fell, 1908.

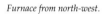

Furnace from north-west.

Furnace loading mouth.

Furnace

The furnace itself stands at the centre of the site and occupies a bankside position. Its general design and function can best be appreciated by comparing a side view of the building with the cut-away and sectional drawings. The principal ingredients used in the iron smelting process—the iron ore, charcoal and limestone flux—were transported from the storage sheds to the high-level charging-house on the south side. Firstly the charcoal was fed into the loading-mouth at the top of the furnace-shaft and a fire lit at the base. The other raw materials were then added. A high-temperature chemical reaction was achieved by means of a continuous upwards blast of air, and the molten iron trickled down through the chimney to the base where it settled in the hearth with the impurities floating on top. It was then drawn off through the wide-splayed aperture in the western side-wall and into moulds prepared in the bed of sand in the casting-house.

It was normal practice to pre-heat or season the furnace about a week in advance of these operations; the hearth area had to be relined where necessary and the

apertures forming the tuyère and tap-hole (see over) then sealed. Once the furnace was put into blast, it was recharged constantly and kept in continuous operation over a period lasting from about late autumn until early summer.

The **charging-house** is entered by a wide door in the south gable. This used to be fronted by a gabled porch as shown by the surviving wall-foundations and the sockets for the roof-timbers in the main south wall. This porch has a cobbled floor and a single narrow iron track in the centre. Slate trackways ran from the iron-ore shed, and the materials required for charging the furnace were assembled on the cobbled platform within the charging-house. They were then measured in the correct proportions ⅕ the ore and limestone by weight and the charcoal by volume and carried across the intervening cavity on a joisted bridge and up the brick-built steps to the radially flared mouth of the furnace-chimney. The floor of the charging-house and the upper works of the furnace have at some period been heightened. A passage, which is floored at the original height, runs around all four sides of the furnace super-structure and is lit by a pair of windows in the north wall.

Situated within the cavity between the charging-house retaining-wall and the furnace below the level of the bridge are the remains of a long narrow chamber. It possessed a timberjoisted floor, a window in the west wall and a doorway in the east wall, access to which was apparently from an external ramp. The most curious feature is a fireplace in the south wall which incorporates a pair of horizontal flues issuing from the side-walls. It has been suggested that this somewhat inconveniently-sited chamber was intended as a bothy for the furnace-master who had to remain in almost constant attendance during the smelting operations.

The **waterwheel**, which provided the motive power for the bellows, was

Former lade running alongside the River Awe.

The **furnace-stack** itself is sturdily constructed of lime-mortared rubble masonry partly laid to courses. The lower half of the walls has a pronounced batter to give extra stability, and the extremes of heat and stress to which the structure was regularly subjected made periodic re-lining and occasional rebuilding inevitable. Not surprisingly, therefore, the head of the chimney and possibly the upper portion of the masonry walling are of secondary (probably nineteenth-century) construction. The firebrick-lined interior may have been replaced after each smelting campaign, which generally lasted throughout each winter from September to April.

Each of the deep splayed openings in the north and west walls is spanned with a system of three cast-iron lintels interspersed for the most part with overhanging slabs of red sandstone. Three of the lintels bear the cast inscription 'BUNAW. F. [Bonawe Furnace] 1753', while the central lintel of the northern (bellows) opening bears what appears to be the letters NE [?Newland] and the date 175[?3]. On the western face the innermost opening, otherwise known as a tymp, was formerly traversed by a slag dam incorporating a clay-plugged tap-hole and the remains of the slag-pot stand at the north-west angle of the forehearth. The blocking of the northern aperture contained the *tuyéres*, the holes through which the blast was admitted from the nozzles of the bellows. The furnace hearth was set at the base of the chimney within an area about 2-4m square. Looking upwards one can see the (later) circular tunnellining carried on curved iron angle-brackets. Some of the facing firebricks bear the stamp of the Cwmbran Fireclay Company, Monmouthshire. The tunnel itself is of bottle-shaped section and tapers gradually from a narrow loading-mouth and throat to a distended belly or crucible 2-7m in maximum diameter. Originally it was probably of an angular profile and incorporated more pronounced *boshes*, that

mounted against the east wall of the blowing-house and was of low breast-shot type, 3-7m in diameter and almost 2m wide. It was removed in 1941, and its position is indicated by the bearing-blocks and mountings on either side of the wheel-pit. The lade, or aqueduct, brought water from the River Awe about 1km to the east, and was carried onto the wheel by a wooden trough, or launder. Beyond the site of the wheel the tail-race runs north-westwards to empty into Loch Etive. Between the charging-house and furnace there is a stone-lined conduit which runs beneath arched openings in the side-walls and extends alongside the casting-floor. It was probably capable of receiving a diverted flow from the main water-course when required for purposes of cooling or insulation, and may have collected seepage from the adjacent retaining walls. It would seem to have ceased whatever function it served early in the nineteenth century and to have been partly filled in.

Reconstruction drawing of the furnace showing working principles.

is, the outward-flaring parts of the shaft immediately above the hearth.

The **blowing-house, casting-house, store** and **smithy,** which surrounded the furnace on its northern and western sides, are now ruinous and very largely reduced to their wall-foundations; of the pitched roofs which formerly covered these ancillary structures only the sockets for the roof-timbers can now be seen in the adjacent walls of the furnace. Excavations have revealed the granite base-blocks of the blowing-engine that was introduced in the nineteenth century to replace the original leather bellows. Both were powered through a camshaft by the waterwheel mounted in the pit on the eastern side. The floor of the casting-house was found to be divided lengthwise; on the north there was a part-metalled floor defined by a sandstone kerb, and on the south a bed of fine sand up to 900mm deep.

The present car-park is situated among the **slag-heaps** which have been quarried for road-making purposes. Much of the visible waste material probably dates from the last phases of the productive life of the furnace. It comprises white limey slags and green vitreous pieces intermixed with fragments of scrap pig iron. Much of the slag can be seen to contain embedded charcoal.

Early view of the furnace from the north.

25

Graded slates on eastern charcoal shed .

Building materials and methods of construction

The walls of the principal buildings are strongly constructed of lime-mortared random or coursed rubble masonry. The local light-grey Bonawe granite is one of the main constituents, but use is also made of a reddish-brown porphyrite, particularly in the later addition to the ore shed. The red sandstone slabs that are much in evidence around the furnace hearth and the adjacent areas may have been specially imported from the Furness district. Firebrick is also used extensively in the construction of the furnace lining and chimney.

On account of their bankside positions, most of the buildings incorporate some form of retaining-wall or revetment built against the natural slope, and, especially on the lower sides, the main load-bearing walls usually either are based on one or more stepped offset-courses or have a pronounced batter. A number of the large doorways are spanned by massive timber lintels, but one of the characteristic building features which is quite clearly of Lakeland origin is the slabstone drip- or hood-mould which appears fairly regularly over the lesser window- and doorway-openings. Some of the floors appear to have been cobbled, but the fact that the floors of the cavity apartments adjacent to the furnace are joisted is perhaps testimony to the belief in the fireproof qualities of large timbers. The most specialised flooring requirement was in the casting-house where the pigs of iron were customarily cast in beds of sand.

All the buildings are slate covered, and the warehouses especially have great expanses of Lakeland slates graded in diminishing courses which have since been systematically renewed. It is known, however, that local Easdale slate from the west coast was also used, but the builders adhered to English practice in nailing the slates to laths or battens and not to close-jointed sarking-boards in accordance with Scottish custom. The slate-hung eaves fascia that is seen on the charcoal sheds and iron-ore shed is also an imported technique.

The roofs, which achieve considerable spans over the storage-sheds, are mainly of collar and tie-beam truss construction, but the greatest internal clear span (30m), that of the eastern charcoal shed, is of a simple but technically accomplished king-post design. Each type of truss is made up of pegged and jointed members and the principal rafters form the bay divisions. Rows of scarf-jointed or butt-ended purlins are carried on the backs of the main rafters, while the tie-beams are dovetailed onto the tops of the wall-plates, not a particularly common or traditional technique of construction in Scotland. The outshots or side-aisles have separate roof-structures; the principal raking members are tied into the main wall-head and are secured at the lower end by stub wall-posts.

Distinctive building features at Bonawe.

a King post roof over eastern charcoal shed.

b Details of slate-hung eaves fascia;

c Detail of stub wall-post.

Workers' cottages; paired doorways and ladder-stair.

The following parts of the complex are not in the care of the Secretary of State for Scotland

Workers' housing

The amount and the type of housing provided by the Company must clearly have been related to their industrial requirements. The L-shaped range of two-storeyed tenement-buildings which stand on low-lying ground to the north-east appears to have been erected in three stages during the later eighteenth and nineteenth centuries, the construction of the eastern limb having been followed successively by the central block and the northern limb. The central portion, which has now been modernised and rebuilt, is by tradition the overseer's house, while the remaining parts, which have been gutted by fire, comprised both flatted and storeyed units of three, four or more apartments; the upper flats were reached by forestairs at

the rear. Some of the ancillary buildings to the east were of traditional cruck-framed roof construction.

A terraced row of 1½-storeyed cottages, which stands on the higher ground south-east of the fenced precinct, may possibly date from the earliest foundation of the ironworks. The row consists of eight two-roomed units which, as can be seen from the positions of the doorways, are grouped together in pairs. Each domestic unit comprises a single living-room on the ground floor with a sleeping-loft above which is reached by a steep ladder stair. Although capable of being run together, these dwellings were thus designed to provide only limited accommodation, perhaps bothies for skilled workmen living on their own or with small families.

Manager's house

Bonawe House is situated in private wooded policies about 300m east-south-east of the main group of furnace buildings. This is the mansion that was 'built by a Mr Knott [Michael Knott, d. 1772] of Coniston Water-head, a partner in the iron-foundry at Bonawe'. The house underwent further modifications and extensions, but the original mid-eighteenth century nucleus consists of a fairly plain three-storeyed five-bay block. In 1803 Dorothy Wordsworth saw fit to describe it as 'an ugly yellow-daubed building, staring this way and that'.

Quay

The quay, which is situated over 300m north-west of the furnace, extends some 130m into the waters of Loch Etive from the east shore of Airds Bay. This was where the iron ore was unloaded from sailing-ships and the pig iron embarked for the return voyage to England. The quay is of mortared masonry construction, and is complete with mooring-rings, stairs and an expanded west terminal where there are also the surviving timber-supports of a later wooden landing-stage.

28

Bonawe House, the works' manager's house, from north-west.

The main stables-block, a horse-engine and adjacent meal store or 'truck shop' lie to the east of the track which runs from the quay to the furnace, and other ancillary structures, which have now largely disappeared, are known to have occupied sites on either side of this route. He also are traces of run-rig, or ploughing, arising from the cultivation by the workforce of cereal and vegetable crops.

'Benawe, Loch Etive, from near Tyanuilt' by T Allom, engraved by H Griffith, 1836 (from W Beattie, Scotland Illustrated, 1838, vol 2, pl 32).

Other Sites of Related Interest

Red Smiddy, Poolewe, Ross and Cromarty (NGR NG 861797).
Slight remains of probably the first Scottish charcoal-fired blast-furnace, established before 1610 by Sir George Hay.
Glen Kinglass, Argyll (NGR NN 082371).
Remains of ironworks (furnace mainly) associated with short-lived enterprise about 1722 to about 1738. The immediate predecessor of Bonawe on Loch Etive.
Craleckan Furnace, Mid Argyll (NGR NN 025001).
The last of the charcoal-based ironworks to be built in the Scottish Highlands, about 1754 to about 1813. Founded and operated by the Duddon Furnace Company.
Tarrioch Ironworks, Cumnock and Doon Valley (NGR NS 642269).
Vestiges of what are thought to have been the only charcoal-fired blast-furnace in southern Scotland. Founded possibly in about 1732 by the third Earl of Cathcart.
Duddon Bridge, Cumbria (NGR SD 1968-83). The most complete surviving example of the charcoal ironworks in Fumess district, 1736-1867.
Coalbrookdale Furnace, Ironbridge, Salop (NGR SJ 667047).
The scene of the first successful smelting of iron ore in 1709 using coke instead of charcoal as fuel. The old furnace was probably rebuilt in 1777 and again after 1801. *Open to the public, Ironbridge Gorge Museum Trust.*
Duddon Bridge Ironworks, Cumbria.
Dyfi Furnace, near Aberystwyth, Dyfed (NGR SN 685951) The best preserved charcoal blast-furnace in Wales, founded in 1755. *Open to the public, CADW.*

The blowing-arch and blow-hole at Craleckan Furnace, Argyll.

Duddon Bridge Ironworks, Cumbria.

Dyfi Furnace, Dyfed.

Further Reading

D Diderot, *L'Encyclopédie, ou Dictionnaire Raisonné des Sciences, des Arts et des Métiers* (1763), translated selections from the Manufacturing and Technical Arts in C C Gillispie (ed), *A Diderot Pictorial Encyclopaedia of Trades and Industry* (1959) 24-25 and 82-121

J H Dixon, *Gairloch* (1886) 72-96

A Fell, *The Early Iron Industry of Furness and District* (1908)

W K V Gale, *The British Iron and Steel Industry* (1967)

W K V Gale, *Iron and Steel* (1969)

G D Hay and G P Stell, *Monuments of Industry* (1986) 108-114

J H Lewis, 'The charcoal-fired blast-furnaces of Scotland: A review', *Proceedings of the Society of Antiquaries of Scotland*, 114 (1984) 433-79

J M Lindsay, 'Charcoal iron smelting and its fuel supply; the example of Lorn Furnace, Argyllshire, 1753-1876', *Journal of Historical Geography* (1975), 283-98

J M Lindsay, 'The iron industry in the Highlands; charcoal blast furnaces', *Scottish Historical Review*, 56, part 1 (April 1977) 49-63

W I Macadam, 'Notes on the ancient iron industry of Scotland', *Proceedings of the Society of Antiquaries of Scotland*, 21(1886-87) 89-131 National Library of Scotland, Adv. MSS 993-95, Lorn Furnace Company Papers (including letterbooks 1786-1812)

Royal Commission on the Ancient and Historical Monuments of Scotland, *Inventory of Argyll ii, Lorn* (1975), no 362

H R Schubert, *History of the British Iron and Steel Industry from c. 450 BC to AD 1775* (1957) R F Tylecote, *A History of Metallurgy* (1976)

Acknowledgements

Grateful thanks for permission to reproduce photographs to:
Cadw: Welsh Historic Monuments (page 31 bottom).
Forestry Commission (page 8).
John R Hume (pages 9 left and 14 top).
John Lewis (page 31 middle).
Kunsthistorisches Museum, Vienna (page 4).
The Royal Commission on the Ancient and Historical Monuments of Scotland (pages 16-17, 18 bottom,20, 23, 25 top, 26, 27 and 28).
The Trustees of the National Library of Scotland (page 12).

First Published by HMSO 1984
This impression first published by Historic Scotland 1995
Copyright © Historic Scotland 1995
ISBN 1 900168 03 0